life balance

GET IT THE

F_____

TOGETHER

FITNESS - FAMILY - FUN - FINANCE

Marlisa Brown
MS, RD, CDE, CDN

Get It The F___ Together: Fitness-Family-Fun-Finance
Actionable Steps to Achieving Life Balance

Marlisa Brown, MS, RD, CDE, CDN

Published by:
Total Wellness, Inc.
375 Commack Road, suite # 201
Deer Park, NY 11729
www.TWellness.net 631-666-4297

This book is not intended as a replacement for care from a health professional. None of the information in this book should be considered personal medical or financial advice. Provided here are thought provoking questions, and strategies to help you toward the quest of life balance; fitness, family, fun, finance.

If you have been diagnosed or are experiencing a medical issue, please consult your personal physician for medical clearance before making any of the dietary and/or lifestyle changes discussed in this book.
If you are experiencing financial issues, please consult with a certified financial planner to help with any of your investment questions.
Neither the author nor the publisher shall be liable for any loss or damage allegedly arising as a result of your use of any information in this book.

ISBN: 978-0-9975428-0-6

Interested in having Marlisa speak at your organization?
www.MarlisaSpeaks.com

Dedicated in memory to my parents,
Anna and Stuart Brown.

For over 50 years, they clung close to each other as they faced and survived many difficult obstacles together. They lived; they loved; they laughed; they cried. They are forever missed in my heart.

Acknowledgments

I want to extend special thanks to those who helped make this book possible.

Firstly Jacqueline Gutierrez for her continuous support to help me bring this book to life. Jackie contributed to every step from edits, to layout, to images and cover. I cannot thank her enough. In addition I want to thank Carol Murray for her support and promotional help, Julia Pastore for her editing and encouragement, Marilyn Hall for her book review and Derek Brown for his artistic eye.

"You are never as good alone as you can be with the talented people around you."

Contents

Introduction

Let's face it. There are times in everybody's life when it feels as if your world is falling apart. During these times you may think that the grass is greener elsewhere. But is it really? Sometimes it seems all life can offer us is a never-ending number of difficulties, arranged like a set of Dominoes tiles. When one tile falls, the others fall one after another. How you handle these moments determines how your future will unfold. Don't get me wrong. Difficulties are not all the same. Some people really do get hit with heavier burdens than others. But, no matter what you are facing, the principles for recovery are the same.

In my life, there were moments when I have felt as though I was on a rollercoaster. At times I was on my way up and other times I was dropping fast. Tragedy struck early in my childhood and it took me many years to recover. In later years, I was lucky enough to experience close friendships, good health, an exciting career, and a wonderful man in my life. You might call this period in my life, "the ZONE."

As my business continued to grow, I helped my clients become successful, wrote books, built my private practice, and felt as though I would be set in just a few short years. Unfortunately, I was mistaken. My dominoes started to fall during the aftermath of the World Trade Center tragedy. I lost over 70% of my business due to the many industry-related crashes and the hits kept on coming. I experienced one loss after another, after another, over a two-year period.

It took me years to reboot and reestablish myself. Working all the time, I was able to pull myself out. However, like so many others, I neglected other parts of my life, sacrificing my health and social activities in order to stabilize my business. Then just when I thought I could see my way clear, I was hit with the recession and changes to the health care industry which pushed my business back again. My personal life started to fall apart, and I was given the worst hit of all: the heartbreaking loss of my parents.

During difficult time in our lives it is hard to think clearly and make sense of it all. Looking back, I realize that although none of these events were in my control and the burden *was* heavy, I could have made it easier on myself. There were steps I could have taken to help me get through this time. Instead, I was letting events shape my life and I was putting out fires one at a time. Time was speeding forward and with the constant firefighting, I found myself getting more out of shape, losing money, and facing serious personal relationship issues. I realize now that in order to find my way out, I needed to put myself on a path with clear focus, a life plan that I could follow even when tragic obstacles were thrown in my way.

I have always found that when you are down and out more difficulties are thrown in your way. This time was no different. Additional obstacles and challenges kept appearing. I had a bad fall that led to a blood infection lasting for more than a year. I was forced to move my office to a new location, adding to my stress. Then, I cracked a tooth but didn't even realize it until it too got infected. I left the dentist's office and got into a nasty car accident and injured my neck. The pain interfered with my writing and speaking work. Of course, the series of unfortunate events continued like a bad movie. I got a horrible case of poison ivy which lasted for months and delayed the physical therapy treatments for my neck. Needless to say, I had been neglecting my personal life, and so I was looking at the very real possibility of being single again. To top it off, my office assistant had to quit suddenly due to a family illness.

I felt overwhelmed and couldn't see my way clear. My vision and thinking were clouded. I had gone from looking at a bright future to the dark void of the unknown. I seemed to be stuck in a hole and I hadn't found the rope to pull myself out yet. How could this have happened? When I reflect back, it tells its own story. The personal hits and the many hours working put me under constant stress. I neglected what was most important to me and found myself skipping social time and overlooking needed health matters, which contributed to additional problems and medical issues and in a vicious cycle.

I was stuck. Newton's first law of motion states that every item at rest will remain at rest, or an item in motion will stay in uniform motion in a straight line, unless it is compelled to change its state by an external force. The external force or moment that finally woke me up to reality (or when I hit rock bottom) came when I was traveling on the subway. When I arrived at my stop, the escalator was out of order and there was a huge staircase that I needed to climb to reach the street. Given I was feeling run down and I was carrying several heavy bags with me, it seemed like an impossible task. I waited until everyone had gone up the stairs so my way was clear and then slowly started my climb. Short of breath, I rested every few steps. This staircase shouldn't have been so difficult, but the neglect to my health, the infection in my leg, and the extra weight I was carrying (I was the heaviest I have ever been in my life—not so funny for a dietitian) put me in a compromised state. As I climbed, I found myself actually thinking, will I be able to make it to the street? Moments before I made it to the top another train arrived in the station and an anxious group of millennials started up the narrow stairwell behind me. I pushed myself to go faster and as I did so my shoe fell off and tumbled down to the bottom of the steps. I remember thinking to myself that I may need to find a shoe store nearby because I wouldn't be able to make it all the way down the staircase and then back up again. Thankfully, a good Samaritan took pity on me and brought my shoe to me.

When I finally reached my destination, I went into the ladies' room to pull myself together. I looked into the mirror in disgust and said out loud: GET IT THE F____ TOGETHER. For over 2 1/2 decades I have successfully helped more than 20,000 people with their health, personal, and financial issues and I have rebooted my ocareer in the face of extreme difficulties. How did I get here?

I thought on this over the next few weeks and then one day a patient came into my office and shared her feelings about the loss of a dear departed uncle. She told me that family and friends had been by her uncle's side to say goodbye before he passed and he comforted them with the following words: "Don't be sad. It is time for me to go. I am ready. I have had a wonderful life and I leave here knowing that I have had everything I would ever want out of this world." What more could anyone ever want? Her uncle's statement summed up everything that was most important in life. What would I have to do to get to a place like that?

At that moment, I realized that the tools I used with my patients would work for me. I already had everything I needed to accomplish my goals and it was time to put an action plan into gear. I focused and formatted my path. I found the rope I needed to pull myself out.

The first step was to practice what I preach:

Work with What You Have
Plan for What You Want
So You Can Live What You Dream

I identified my strengths, weaknesses, needs, and wants. I focused on my goals and identified workable simple steps to achieve them. My action plan included:

1. Taking better care of my health.

2. Stabilizing my business and finances.

3. Spending more time with family and friends.

4. Having more fun.

I laid out a timeline and designed tools which helped me to focus. With an action plan in place, my business more than doubled within a year. I made sure every step I took always put my health and family matters first. It's true. Without your health you have nothing. Today I may not be running marathons or wearing a bikini, but I no longer have trouble going up a flight of stairs or doing any of my day-to-day activities. I make my doctor's appointments and I rest and de-stress when I need to. Above all, I always find time for social events and for my friends and family.

In this book, I will share with you the tools that

helped me and the thousands of others I have worked with. This program takes into account that each person is different and allows you to identify what is most important to you, in order to customize a plan to give you more success, happiness, and health. No one has a perfect journey but with focus, persistence, and vision, you can get what you need to be happy.

When life throws you road blocks…Get it the F___ together.

Healthy regards,

Marlisa

Chapter I. FOCUS

If you don't know where you are going, how can you ever expect to get there?

The most important tool you can have in your toolkit before starting something new is focus. With focus, you'll have a clear vision of what you want and how you plan to get it. First, you'll do a self-evaluation in order to find out what matters to you the most. It's difficult to be clearheaded when life seems to be falling apart and too many things are happening at the same time. To make it easier to find your focus, let's break it down into simple steps.

Find Your Focus

Step 1. Set your priorities so you know where you want to go.

Step 2. Put your priorities in order of importance.

Step 3. Identify exactly what each priority means to you.

Step 4. Break down each priority into small actionable steps.

Step 5. Determine if you have the time available to implement your plan.

Step 1.
   Set your priorities so you know where you want to go.

Start by picking a goal, anything that may be important to you. It can be as general (I want to make more money) or as specific as you want (I want to pay off my credit card). The most important thing is to define a goal. Too many people start moving without really knowing anything about where they are going. These folks usually end up lost. While it's sometimes true that any movement may be better than none at all, by lasering in on specific goals, you'll be more likely to accomplish them.

Make a list of the things that are the most important for you to achieve. This helps you find your focus.

My Priority List:

   - Take care of my health

   - Spend more time having fun

   - Repair business issues

   - Spend more time with family and friends

Step 2.
   Put your priorities in order of importance.

My Priority List in Order of Importance:

1. Take care of my health

2. Repair business issues

3. Spend more time with family and friends

4. Spend more time having fun

Step 3.
Identify exactly what each priority means to you.

If I identify health as the number one item on my priority list, what does that mean to me? Change my diet? Exercise more? Lower my cholesterol? Lose weight? Have more energy? Take my medications as prescribed? Working on your health can mean different things to different people. Identify what it means to you.

To me it meant:

- eating better

- exercising more

- increasing my energy

If I identify family as my priority, what would that mean to me? It may seem like a complete thought or a specific focus but is it? Do I mean my kids, parents, grandparents, spouse, or friends? Do I mean I need to spend more time with them? Come up with money for them? Help plan their future? "Family" as a priority isn't focused enough. If you want to achieve something, you need to spell out what exactly what it means to you. If you want to get there, you need to know what you want. When I listed family and friends, I meant I wanted to spend more quality time with them whenever possible and to be there for them whenever they need me. I wanted to overlook silly things that made me argue with my relatives and, above all, I wanted to make our time together count, showing how much we mean to each other.

If business is my priority, I might mean that I need to determine what to do to cover my overhead. Or, what to do to pay off debt or take a salary that covers my living expenses. Or, what to do to make it so I have more time off and to have an assistant who can manage all my day to day operations. As you can see, a goal can mean many different things. Identify exactly what it means to you.

Step 4.

> *Break each item down on my list into small actionable steps.*

Once you know exactly what your goals mean to you, you can figure out the steps you need to take to accomplish them.

For example, if your number one priority is to be in

better shape and to you that means losing weight, what are the steps you will need to make that happen?

Exercise?
Change your eating habits?
Drink more water?

This list is a good start but it's still too general. You need actionable steps.

How will you exercise? When will you exercise? What kind of exercise will you do? How often will you do it? Now do the same for each item. How will you change your eating habits? When will you get started? Will you cook more, take a cooking class, or hire someone to bring you healthy foods?

As you can see, just saying you will change your eating habits is not enough. You need to know the specific details and the steps involved. Let's add more specifics for how to change your eating habits.

> - One day each weekend, you will pre-prepare healthy foods for lunch and dinner for the week.

> - You will also locate several restaurants in your area that provide healthier alternatives and will usually select from those restaurants when you go out.

> - You will stock healthier snacks in your

home and keep trigger foods like cookies and chips out of the house.

- You will go to a registered dietitian to make sure you are getting all of the nutrition you need.

- You will allow some treats and cheats one or two times a week so you don't feel deprived.

Making an actionable plan with steps makes it more likely that you will succeed with your goal.

Think about Dorothy in *The Wizard of Oz*.

She knew she wanted to save Toto and to get home to Kansas and Auntie Em. Save Toto first, then find a way to get home. To get home, she needed to follow the yellow brick road and find the Wizard. Even though Dorothy experienced many unforeseen obstacles, twists, and turns along the way, she knew what she wanted and what steps she needed to take to achieve it. No matter what happened, she had a clear focus to continue on. Follow the yellow brick road.

Step 5.

   Determine if you have the time to implement your plan.

So many people tell me there is not enough time for everything they want to accomplish, and that is often true. But in order to accomplish your goals, you must find the time to do the steps necessary to achieve them.

In Chapter II, I'll show you how to evaluate how you currently spend your time and help you find more time in your schedule. You may have more time than you think you do.

Meet Steve

Before we move to Chapter II, I would like you to meet Steve, a man who has lost his focus.

> Steve is a smart well-liked guy. He loves his wife and 4-year-old daughter. Providing for his family and spending time with them are very important to Steve. Steve likes to help everyone and has difficulty saying "no." He is very smart with a lot of employment opportunities, but he has gotten locked into working for his dad's struggling business. Working all the time, saying yes to everyone, and putting out fires, Steve finds no time for his family or friends. He is exhausted and struggles to make ends meet. He is letting events shape his life and is missing out on what is most important to him.

> See how Steve turns his life around in Chapter VII: Finance.

Finding your focus and developing an action plan will enable you to achieve what is most important to you.

FOCUS WORKSHEET:

Step 1. Set your priorities:

_____

_____

_____

_____

_____

_____

_____

Step 2. List your top priorities in order of importance:

_____

_____

_____

_____

_____

_____

*Step 3. Break each item on your priority list
into actionable steps:*

_____

_____

_____

_____

_____

_____

_____

*Step 4. Determine if you have the time to
accomplish your priority items:*

_____

_____

_____

*Step 5. Determine if you have the time to
achieve your goals:*

_____

_____

_____

_____

Chapter II.   FINDING TIME

Before you can find the time to do what you want, you'll need to know where all of your time is usually spent. You may think you know what happens to it—but do you really?

Time speeds forward like an express train and is gone as quickly as it passes. For most of us, the endless list of things to do may seem to carry over day after day, again and again. Even when it seems like we can get everything accomplished, something almost always gets in the way and stops us. There is hardly any space for new things or those extra things that we want to do. Life seems to be full of musts and need tos with little time for our want tos.

In order to take control of your life and to achieve what you truly want, you must first carefully evaluate how you spend your time. This includes identifying needs, fine-tuning daily activities, and modifying your time usage. These strategies make it possible for you to succeed and reach your goals. Let me share with you an action plan to evaluate your time that has worked for so many of my clients.

In Chapter I, we spent a lot of time looking at goals, focus, and direction. Using focus to identify our destination, we listed our life priorities and organized them in order of importance. Next, we specified exactly what they mean to us and broke down our goals into actionable steps. Now, with Step 5, we need to determine if we have the necessary time in our schedules to take those steps and, if at first glance it appears we do not, we need to find the time. Let's use my example from Chapter I to help us take a closer look at time management.

Step 1.
Set your priorities so you know where you want to go.

My Priority List:

- Take better care of my health

- Spend more time having fun

- Repair business issues

- Spend more time with family and friends

Note that this is a list of things that I want to accomplish in general. They are not in order of importance and there are no details for how to achieve these goals.

Step 2.
Put your priorities in order of importance.

My Priority List in Order of Importance:

1. Take better care of my health

2. Repair business issues

3. Spend more time with family and friends

4. Spend more time having fun

As you can see, I have listed the things that I want in the order that is most important to me.

Step 3.
Identify exactly what each priority means to you.

My first priority is taking better care of my health. I need to breakdown what that means to me:

- eating better

- exercising more

- increasing my energy

As you can see, for each item on my priority list I need to identify exactly what that means to me.

Step 4.
Break down each priority into small actionable steps.

My Priority List Broken Down into Actionable Steps:

1. Health

   - walk daily and go to gym 3-4x each week

   - prepare fresh healthy foods

   - get enough sleep

   - make doctor's appointments

2. Business

   - do a break-even analysis

   - increase profitability by cutting overhead

   - decrease wasted time by delegating more

   - plan for the future with short and long - term goals

3. Family and Friends

   - see them more often

   - plan social events

   - be available when needed

   - Fun

   - plan at least one fun activity every week

- do one fun activity daily (such as playing with my dog)

Now that I've determined the actionable steps I need to take, I have to find the time to take them.

Note, before you determine if you have the time to implement your plan make sure you also have all the resources you need to get started. Resources are the tools that will be needed to go forward with your plan such as credit, money, knowledge, education, workers, etc. So for example I had listed health as one of my priorities and my actionable steps were; exercise, healthy eating, sleep and doctor visits. In order to identify if there are resources I would need to get started there are some questions that should be asked. For example in order to exercise do I need to join a gym or buy exercise equipment? For healthy eating, do I know how to cook healthy and do I have the money to buy healthier foods? For getting enough sleep do I need a new mattress or medications to help me sleep? To make my doctor visits, do I have health insurance or money to pay for these visits? If I have the resources to start my plan and my priorities spelled out with actionable steps I can now work on finding the time to implement my plan.

Step 5.
Determine if you have the time to implement your plan.

First, do a complete assessment of how you currently spend your time. Make sure you keep a daily diary for at least one week noting all of your activities and the time spent on them. Include everything: sleeping, eating, dressing, commuting, social media, *everything* that you do daily. Leave nothing out. These details show where you may be wasting time and where you are spending it wisely.

My Time Assessment

This is an example of a typical 24-hour weekday. In order to make it easier for you to follow I have listed things very briefly below, none of the details are included. When you work on your journal break things down further. For example if I noted that I spent 1 hour running errands in my journal I should give all the details of that activity such as; My daily errands which include, 35 minutes picking up food, 10 minutes at the dry cleaners,10 minutes at the bank, 5 minutes driving home which adds up to my 1 hour worth of errands. If I just estimate my time spent I am surely going to miss something.

My Daily Time Usage
8 hours sleeping
1 ½ hours mindless time wasting: text messaging, emails, social media, television etc.
8 hours at work
2 hours commuting
1 hour running errands
3 hours misc. personal items: phone calls, food prep, eating
½ hour decompressing at home when I'm back from work

Total Time Spent Per Day= 24 Hours.

When you look at how I spend my time in an average 24-hour workday, you can see all 24 hours are used up and I haven't worked on anything listed on my priority list or action plan.

If I'm booked solid for 24 out of 24 hours in the day, how can I achieve anything extra that I want? Simple: I can't! By spending my time in this way it's no wonder I can't get to anything I want and my to-do list keeps on growing.

I need to find a new way to spend my time to work on the things that matter to me the most.

Step 6.
Find the time you need.

Where can I save time?

After reviewing my activities, I decided there were items that could be changed and simplified to free up some time.

For example, I wasted 1 ½ hours each day checking my messages and emails continuously and watching television. I needed to curb the time I spent on these activities and use it to accomplish what I really wanted. I had to stop wasting valuable time on mindless activities. This waste was keeping me from achieving the things that were most important to me, the things that I wanted most of all. If I didn't change something now there would never be time available for my health, business innovations, family or fun time. Looking even more closely, I realized I was wasting time everywhere.

Trim back & be more mindful

The obvious place to start trimming and being more mindful was with those 1 ½ hours of mindless activities. I could be more careful and cut that down to ½ hour a day. Time saved: **1 hour each workday.**

I could better manage my errands by doing them every other day instead of daily and doing them in a more organized, efficient manner. Time saved: **½ hour each workday.**

Instead of driving to work each day, I could join a car pool or take mass transit so I could get some work done *en route*, giving me more free time later.

Time saved: ½ **hour each workday**.

I could trim my 3 hours of personal time daily to 2 ½ hours. Time saved: ½ **hour each workday**.

Everything else needed to stay as is.

Even so, I have identified **2 ½ hours of time each workday** to dedicate to my action plan
(1 + ½ + ½ + ½ = 2 1/2 hours each workday).

For a 5-day work week that means: **12 ½ hours saved**.

My Daily Time Usage on Weekends
8 hours sleeping 1 ½ hours mindless time wasting: text messaging, emails, social media, television etc. 3 hours family and friends 3 hours house chores 1 hour running errands 3 hours misc. personal items: phone calls, food prep, eating ½ hour decompressing at home when I'm back from work

Total Time Spent Per Weekend Day= 20 Hours.

So per the above breakdown I spend 20 out of 24 on typical weekend days. I have 4 extra hours + 2 hours that I can save based on my weekday calculations (not 2 1/2 because commuting time has been removed) this gives me = 6 hours each weekend day x 2 weekend days = **12 hours saved**.

Consider this: **12 1/2 hours saved on weekdays + 12 hours saved on weekends = 24 1/2 extra hours** to spend each week on my priorities. That's more than one day!

I have more time than I thought but to get things done I really need to budget my time wisely each day. Think of time as money: where can you cut back? How would you like to spend it? Budget wisely.

How can you reduce wasted time?

Step 7.
Decide how to spend your time.

How should I spend my time?

Based on my priorities and action steps, I decided to spend the additional time I'd found as follows:

1. Health: I want to include all the following weekly.

5 hours per week for exercise: ½ hour of exercise daily, plus 3 times during the week I'd bump it up to an hour.

2 hours per week to plan healthier meals.

4 hours per week to make my doctor's and other health-related or miscellaneous appointments as needed. Something always comes up.

Total: 11 hours per week allotted for health goals and appointments.

2. Business: I want to fine-tune my time management in order to be more productive at work. I will do this by bringing in consultants, delegating more and setting up focus groups. Although I would like to do everything in 8 hours, it's not always possible. Life happens. I want to have more flexibility here so I will allow an extra 4 hours each week here.

Total: 4 hours per week for implementing my business goals.

3. Family and Friends: My family and friends are very important to me. Although I do plan some time for them on weekends, I would like to include more time for them every day. This includes more time for casually catching up, helping each other eating together and more. I would like to add an hour every day here.

Total: 7 additional hours per week will be for family and friends.

4. Fun: We should all include something fun every day. Fun helps to reduce stress, relieves tension can perk you up, makes you feel good and it can provide a needed release. Most of us don't spend enough time having fun. I would like to change this and will budget ½ hour for something fun and enjoyable weekdays plus 2 additional hours weekly for an additional activity such as going to a comedy club.

Total: 4 ½ hours per week on fun activities.

So what do I want to spend extra time on weekly?

Health:	+11 hours
Business:	+ 4 hours
Family & Friends:	+ 7 hours
Fun:	+ 4 1/2 hours

Total Extra Hours Needed Weekly = 26 1/2 Hours

When I budget or estimate anything, I follow a 20/10 rule. I estimate that I am 20% wrong and allow myself 10% of wiggle room (plus or minus) for good measure. In this case, my range would be:

PLUS: 26.5 hours plus 20% (5.3 hours) plus 10% (2.65) hours = 34.45 hours

MINUS: 26.5 hours - 20% (5.3 hours) minus 10% (2.65 hours) = 18.55 hours

Roughly, I need between 18.55 to 34.45 hours to work on my goals. In some cases, I may change my plan based on these calculations but in this situation, I feel comfortable with the 26 1/2 hours that I have determined I need.

Note that this timeline does not allow for special add ons such as: last minute plans, holidays, weddings, etc.

Remember, earlier on I had found that with careful planning I could save a possible 24 1/2 extra hours each week. According to my current plan I need 26 1/2 hours. I'm 2 hours short. It's like I don't have enough money at the supermarket so I have to take something out of my cart.

What do I want to take off my list, after all I only have 24 ½ hours? I must prioritize on where to spend my time first.

Keep in mind that no matter what your timeline,

there will always be lost time; things will happen that you didn't anticipate and you may use up available time sooner than you expect. This is why you must prioritize so the most important things happen first; you don't want to go off track and miss implementing priority items. If you find that you are continuously being thrown off your schedule, take another look at your priorities and action steps to give yourself the time you need to make progress on at least some of your priorities and goals.

Focus on one or two action steps and make sure you have time in your schedule to complete those first. It's important not to dump everything on your plate all at once. If you overwhelm yourself you may freeze up and be unable to accomplish anything at all. Creating and revising a timeline is very tedious and isn't easy to do. You really have to work hard to establish a manageable timeline and stick with it (or adjust it as needed) but in the end it will be worth it.

To help keep you on track use a daily calendar to list listing all of your daily activities in order to re-evaluate your plan weekly. Record any changes to your plan and trim back on your scheduled time as needed in order to meet your top priorities. If you feel that right now life is really knocking you down that is what Get it the F___ Together is all about! This is the time to take back control. Using this breakdown of time is a *must* to help get you back on track.

Here's the timeline I used to re-evaluate my priorities to make sure I had enough time for what mattered to me the most; exercise, spending time with family and friends, and fun. So to start plugged these items into my calendar first:

Monday, 2 1/2 hours available: 1 hour gym + 1 hour family and friends + ½ hour fun

= 2 1/2 hours ✓

Tuesday, 2 1/2 hours available: ½ hour exercise + 1 hour family and friends + ½ hour fun = 2 hours (1/2 hour left)

Wednesday, 2.5 hours available: ½ hour exercise + 1 hour family and friends + ½ hour fun = 2 hours (1/2 hour left)

Thursday, 2.5 hours available: 1 hour gym + 1 hour family and friends + ½ hour fun = 2 1/2 hours ✓

Friday, 2.5 hours available: ½ hour exercise + 1 hour family and friends + ½ hour fun = 2 hours (1/2 hour left)

Saturday, 6 hours available: 1 hour gym + 1 hour family and friends + ½ hour fun = 2 1/2 hours (3.5 hours left)

Sunday, 6 hours available: ½ hour exercise + 1 hour family and friends + ½ hour fun = 2 hours (4 hours left)

Total: 9 hours still available to use.

Once I allocated time for my top three priorities, I had 9 hours left. I then identified another priority and did this exercise again and again until those hours were spent. Doing this exercise will help you create a workable schedule to meet your priorities.

Step 8.
Change as needed.

Sometimes you may need to change your plan based on the time and resources you have available. You may even decide to take a priority or action step off your list to be more realistic and to allow for life changes. This is normal and you should expect that your priority list will often change as life changes.

> Your list today may be totally different then next year. For example, if you are in your 20s and in great health, you may not even include health on your list of priorities, or if you live with your parents you may not even consider finances.

> Consider the way you view your priorities today they might change instantly. Instead of a set list of the things you want on one side of the paper and then your time allotment on the other side. The model may look much more like a rotating circle at a fun house. You have an action plan but life gives your list a spin revolving and spinning like a roulette wheel, the circle rotates as life and events push it around. Instead of a

list in a set order of importance, the order keeps changing.

**Priorities change as your life changes.
New things get added and wants and needs swirl, spin, and change without notice.
That is why goals, focus and time allotment need to be reviewed and updated on a regular basis in order to stay on point.**

Focus: 18-year old
living at home
with parents

Focus: 28-year old
father with a
new baby

Your list is a moving circle, rotating and changing as life does. Don't be afraid to adapt and change. At some point, something so important yet unexpected hits us square in the face and ruins all of our pre-conceived action plans. That's okay. Just start fresh and make a new action plan.

Spend Your Time More Efficiently.

Our time is very precious and we must make the best use of it. So far we have covered ways of saving time; now we are going to focus on using it more efficiently. The first step is looking at ways time can escape us.

Have you ever had a really busy day with no time to breathe and at the end of that day you weren't sure what you did with your time? And to top things off you didn't really accomplish anything? That can occur in part because of the daily must-dos and distractions that eat up time.

Must-Dos: Must-dos are what we need to do every day such as eating, sleeping, working, bathing, personal care, and attending to family matters. We learned many of these, let's call them required habits, when we were very young. You probably remember being reminded over and over to do must-dos such as: did you brush your teeth? Did you wash your hands? Did you do your homework? These daily must-do functions make it possible for us to be appropriate in the social structure of the world. They drain some of our time but are needed daily and must be maintained.

Daily Distractions & Bad Habits:

Then there are daily distractions or interruptions. These include continuous cell beeps, flat tires, bad weather, sickness, or problems at home. These are things that we didn't plan for but drain our time and energy. And let's not forget those bad habits that we may do over and over which also drain time such as biting our nails, playing online games, and mindlessly watching television shows. Some distractions, like bad weather, are beyond your control. Limit the ones that you can change and take a closer look at your bad habits and trim back there. Think about which things you can you eliminate and find ways to spend that time more wisely?

Using Autopilot to Your Advantage:

Why time flies: We are so inundated with stimuli every day it becomes too much for us to process without being in a constant state of stress. Therefore our brains ignore the things that it deems to be unimportant, such as noise and interruptions, so we don't feel overwhelmed. It's a form of autopilot. This helps us to go forward focused on key tasks and ignoring distractions happening around us.

Did you ever notice the first time you drive to a new place it always seems to take so much longer to get there than on future trips? This is because the first time you go to a new destination you don't know the area or what to pay attention to, so you take everything in. When you don't know where you are going or what you will encounter on the way, your brain is working hard to make sure you don't miss anything that may be important. On your next trip to the same destination, you are familiar with the route and your brain starts to weed things out things that it feels are unimportant to your journey making it feel as though the trip is shorter. Unfortunately for those of us who live with a repetitive schedule this works against us making our time feel like it is flying by. In life it is important to feel as though each moment counts. To help slow things down to embrace each moment consider this. Our brains work in a continuous state of comparison with each subsequent similar activity seeming to go faster than the last. This makes life and time feel like it is going by faster and faster. Therefore it is important to use auto pilot more efficiently to your advantage. Using autopilot when needed for efficiency but regularly fitting in new activities whenever you can. When you continuously adding new or different activities to your life helps it to feel like there is more time every day.

Working on autopilot frees up your brain to process other thoughts which is good to know when looking for ways to spend time more efficiently. It's not *always* a good thing. You can waste time on autopilot with learned bad habits. But you can use autopilot to more efficiently complete the steps in your action plan and accomplish your goals in less time.

Think back to those times gone by when your grandmother had a set routine she did every day, and she perfected it. She knew the tasks that were most important for her to accomplish each day and she accomplished them in the most efficient way possible. She was very busy all day but her work was defined by a set routine. It wasn't glamorous but it worked for her. She started early in the morning after having breakfast with grandpa and sending him to work with a bagged lunch. She cleaned the entire house, made every meal from scratch, took her little cart to the supermarket, washed clothes, hand-pressed shirts, read the paper, found time to play cards with friends, made special treats for her grandchildren, hand-sewed buttons and socks, and hand-wrote checks to pay all the bills. And she still found time to sit comfortably on the porch with her rolled down orthopedic stockings and curlers in her hair talking and gossiping with the neighbors. She'd taken care of all her household and family must-dos and had enough time left over to relax and handle any unexpected distractions. This was Grandma on autopilot: no wasted time, no cell phone, no computer, no answering machine, just a defined work routine and face-to-face social interactions. With focus and an efficient use of time, Grandma accomplished all her goals every day.

By assessing our time usage, trimming back wasted time, and prioritizing how we use our available time, we can do the same. Yes, we do have a lot more distractions these days. The key is to acknowledge them and limit them so you can spend your time on what matters most to you. If you don't identify what you really need to do and plan properly, you can end up missing out on what is really important to you.

Where can you trim back wasted time in your own life? Is there a routine you can implement to accomplish tasks more efficiently? How can you use autopilot to your advantage?

Meet Sara

Sara is a 69-year-old grandmother in extremely poor health who has found herself in the position of completely raising her 3 grandchildren, 8- and 10-year-old granddaughters and a 14-year-old grandson. She loves them to death and her entire life is consumed with making sure she is there for them. Nothing else matters to her. Sara tries so hard to do everything for them and spends all of her time taking care of them leaving her no time to take care of herself. She often neglects her own health and has put herself at risk for multiple medical complications. Whenever I talk to Sara about spending some time on herself she says, "I don't care or have time for myself; the only thing that matters to me is to be there for my grandchildren." I replied, "do you realize that by not taking any care of yourself in your current health condition you may not be there for your grandchildren or they may end up having to take care of you?" Sometimes we all need to look at the end result of our actions. Even if we think we are doing right, there could be negative consequences. It was like a lightning bolt hit her; Sara finally got it.

She only needed to take her meds, make her doctor's appointments, and spend 1 to 2 hours a day taking care of her health and nutritional needs to resolve most of her health problems. By making these changes, she was able to be there for her #1 goal, her grandchildren. This ah-ha moment was all Sara needed to put herself on track to reach her goals.

Recap: Find Your Focus and Develop on Action Plan to Reach Your Goals

Step 1. Set your priorities so you know where you want to go.

Step 2. Put your priorities in order of importance.

Step 3. Identify exactly what each priority means to you.

Step 4. Break down each priority into small actionable steps.

Step 5. Determine if you have the time to implement your plan.

Step 6. Find the time you need.

Step 7. Decide how to spend your time.

Step 8. Change as needed.

It's time to get going!

TIME MANAGEMENT WORKSHEET:

Refer to the worksheet in Chapter I. After you've identified your priority items and put them in order of importance, determine your actionable steps.

NOTES:_____

_____

_____

_____

_____

_____

_____

Now do a current assessment of your daily time expenditure. Be honest and include everything.

Your Daily Time Usage

Sleep_____

Social Media_____

TV_____

Commuting_____

Work_____

Errands_____

Phone calls_____

Food prep_____

Eating_____

Personal Care_____

Decompressing_____

_____

Other_____

_____

NOTES:_____

Review your list of how you spend time and note where you can save some time:

_____

_____

_____

Map out how you would like to spend your found time (remember time is money):

_____

_____

_____

_____

List your daily distractions and strategies you can use to reduce them in the future:

_____

_____

_____

_____

Chapter III. FORWARD FOR FITNESS

Being fit basically means that you are able-bodied and in relatively good shape and have the ability to survive in your environment. Depending on your personal goals, your definition of physical fitness may be different from someone else's. In order to move forward and create your fitness plan, you need to first overcome the barriers or obstacles that have stopped and continuously stop you from achieving your goals. Let's explore some strategies that you can use to help you to move forward with your fitness.

To be truly fit you need to consider all of the variables of good health. In general, fitness includes a healthy balance of: foods and fluids (fuel), stress management, and physical fitness (exercise & endurance). Most of us will never achieve a fitness level of 100%. There are so many variables to consider, but with a continuous effort we can bring ourselves as close as possible to optimum health. Some may ask: Is there a tool that can evaluate my fitness level? This is a hard question to answer since most available tools will only look at one or two of the essential components and even then they may not be accurate.

When you look at your health what do you consider? If you are thin does that mean you are healthy? Are you healthy if you complete a triathlon? Are you healthy if you eat healthy foods and walk daily? Just because someone does well in a physical competition doesn't mean that person is also following a good diet, drinking adequate fluids, and incorporating stress management into their life. But it does show physical strength and endurance. The person who eats healthy foods, has low stress, and takes a walk each day may still be in need of additional exercise even though they have many good fitness habits.

We all try to do what works for us and some of us may be in better health than others. Some of us want to make healthy choices but life may get in the way and we may put our healthful changes off. Clearly we are all different and none of us are perfect; we all try to do what we can. I have found through the years that when it comes to health, each individual will want to achieve a different level of fitness with specific goals. It's important to note that no matter what someone achieves, even one step in the right direction is one step closer to good health. When someone comes to me for my help it's not my job to tell them what to do; I'm certainly not perfect and as I see it my job is to get them to where they want to be. If I can help someone to make one small step in a positive direction I am giving them the power of the pivot that helps them to move one notch over to a better place. Consider all things on a scale of 1-10. With that in mind, if you evaluated your exercise effort and found it was at a 3 and you increased it to a 4 you have pivoted over a notch in a healthier direction. Even one small change can provide positive benefits no matter how small the change.

Meet Ralph

Some people are so out of shape it is hard to see their progress when they are making small changes (you have to look deeper). Take my patient Ralph.

Ralph came to my office for a nutrition appointment. He had trouble walking. He had uncontrolled diabetes, extremely high cholesterol, high blood pressure, and was 200 pounds overweight. He had recently had quadruple heart bypass surgery. The first time I met him, he put his finger in my face and said, "If you're going to tell me I can't have prime ribs and donuts I am out of here." Clearly it looked like this would have been an unproductive meeting. I responded to him by saying, "I will see what I can do." If I had become even one bit confrontational I would have totally lost him. Certainly, his approach to me was angry and aggressive and made it hard for me to remain neutral, essential if we were to move forward together. The man in front of me was at a high risk for a heart attack and diabetic complications, but my job wasn't to tell him what he should do. My job was to help him find a way to move in a healthier direction. In his case, I didn't expect that he would become a health fanatic. What I needed to do was make him aware that I could help him without turning his life upside down. Any positive change was all I could hope for. With careful communication, we were able to come to a compromise and we agreed upon small goals. In spite of what Ralph had said, he had shown up for his appointment with me so I knew he was probably willing to do something to get healthier.

He never gave up prime ribs, but he ate them less often. He selected leaner cuts of meat and included more chicken and fish in his diet. He didn't give up donuts but he cut down on how often he ate them, and sometimes he selected lower-fat sweets, such as angel food cake, and sugar-reduced products as an alternative. When we first met, he didn't include any exercise in his life. We had to start very small but in time he was able to walk 20 to 30 minutes every day. He still had many health problems, but his blood sugar levels, cholesterol, and blood pressure all went down. Ralph also lost about 50 pounds and felt a lot better. He wasn't fit, but he was so much more fit then he was from the first time I saw him and he was much more open to additional changes.

Get Started with These Three Questions

When you consider revamping your health plan, you should know that there is no one-size-fits-all plan that will work for everyone—despite what any program says.

We all need to take into account existing health problems, injuries, motivation levels, stamina, likes and dislikes, fears, and family history into our plan selections. Many of us may need to have a medical check-up to see what would be safe for us to do. Let me share what has helped my new patients when they started working on their fitness plan and ways you can utilize these tools for yourself.

There are three questions you should consider when starting a health plan for yourself.

1. Why do you want to create fitness goals or change the ones you have?

When I meet a new patient, the first question I ask them is: what brought you in here today? I ask this in order evaluate what prompted them to take this first step (the first step into my office that is). Sometimes they answer saying "my wife…" or "my doctor made me come here." When they make this type of statement, it indicates that at this moment in time they may not be willing to be personally accountable to change. They may not be very serious or ready for the work ahead and if they do make changes they may be very small. They may not even be able to see the importance of creating fitness goals at this point.

By contrast, if someone answers me by saying, "I came here because my doctor said I am pre-diabetic now and I don't want diabetes," I know by this answer they have a strong desire to change and that they are very motivated and ready to get started. Note that being motivated and ready doesn't ensure that change will take place; it just makes it more likely.

Ask yourself, what brought me here? What is making me look at creating or changing my fitness goals today? Starting here helps you clarify why you are ready to get started now, how hard you may be willing to work, and how important it is for you to go forward.

2. What would you like to accomplish?

The second question I ask patients is: what would you like to accomplish from our visits together? This will spell out what is most important to them—their goals not mine. For example, one person may have many health problems but only indicate one goal such as only wanting to lose weight. The person that had previously said they don't want diabetes already answered this in their first response. They said, "I came here because I am pre-diabetic," and then they stated their goal as "I don't want diabetes." Knowing what they want to accomplish and verbalizing it provides direction for us both.

Ask yourself, what do I want to accomplish with this journey to fitness? Don't over promise yourself too much by selecting unrealistic, unachievable goals. For example, let's say you want to lose 100 pounds. Don't say, "I want to lose 100 pounds in the next four months." It is doubtful that would happen and you will end up feeling disappointed no matter what positive changes you make. Reformat that goal instead by simply saying something like: "I would like to lose 100 pounds over the next year and I am willing to change my diet and exercise routines to help me get there. I also know that I will need to make permanent lifestyle changes in order to keep the weight off. I will make a plan that I can follow easily for my lifetime." Reformatting what you want into manageable pieces with steps to success makes it more possible for you to achieve your goals.

To determine which fitness goals you want to start with consider rating each goal on a scale of 1 to 10. For example: On a scale of 1 to 10 how important is exercise to you right now? If you answer less than a 5 maybe this is something that you shouldn't start with; after all it is not the most important thing to you at this moment. So even though exercise is one of your fitness goals it is not the most important thing to you now, so it will have to wait. However if on a scale of 1-10 losing weight is a 9 you should make this your first step. Always start with what you want the most you are more likely to succeed.

3. How hard are you willing to work to achieve these goals?

The third question I ask patients is: how hard are you willing to work to achieve these goals? Some say, "I will do anything; this is so important to me." Some will say, "I would like to have something strict just to follow now in order to kick things off and then I would like to tapper it down." Others will say, "I'm okay with small changes as long as these changes fit into my current lifestyle." Another person will say, "I don't want to work at all. Can't you just give me some easy changes I can make without turning my life upside down?" Clearly how determined or aggressive someone will be can be the beginning or end of this game.

Ask yourself, how hard are you willing to work on this, and how much time can you dedicate to these changes? Be honest with yourself. If you over-commit you will most likely not be able to sustain the journey and even a small setback may return you to your old habits. The last thing you want to do is overwhelm yourself with too much, frustrating yourself and making it impossible to accomplish anything at all.

Setting Reasonable and Realistic Fitness Goals

When you think of your fitness goals, think back to your past unrealized New Years' resolutions. There are so many people who make the same resolutions year after year after year. Common goals include: losing weight, controlling diabetes, and going to the gym regularly. Of course, for fitness goals, weight loss usually tops the list as the number one goal. Why do so many fitness resolutions end up not happening and being repeated again each year without success?

The answer is simpler then the solution. People are setting themselves up with unrealistic, unachievable goals. To make a change you have to change your current lifestyle to accommodate it. Without a plan in place you will often fail. Focus, as covered in Chapter I, is essential. You need to know where you are going before you can develop a workable action plan. And, as detailed in Chapter II, you must find the time to implement your changes. These steps are needed to make your goals—reasonable and realistic goals—easier to achieve.

1. Identify two to three health goals for the next year. If you have ten goals you want to accomplish, you need to consolidate them into two to three choices which will help make your goals more realistic and achievable.

2. Take a look at your lifestyle to see if your goals are possible. Do you have a life barrier that could be getting in the way, such as long hours at work? Evaluate if you should revise the goals further to fit into your timeline and to make them achievable. Look at what you have to change to make it possible.

3. Make a realistic action plan to implement this

change. You may need to refine the plan by breaking actions steps into several even smaller steps if need be and reassess as you go.

Let's look at this process in action.

Meet Jane

Goal: Jane says she wants to exercise daily and she will start by going to the gym five days a week. **Life Barrier:** She is a single parent working two jobs and caring for a family of four. Sometimes she doesn't even have enough time to get enough sleep and she runs around so much she often skips needed doctor appointments and personal wants. Do you think she will be able to leave her house five days a week to go to the gym? *Probably not.* Meeting this goal would require a change in her work schedule or less time spent with her family or she would need to get up an hour or two earlier every day. For this to work, there really needs to be an easier way to fit exercise into her life. A more realistic goal for her to start with would be something like this: a commitment to stretch for 5 minutes every morning, take a 10- or 20- or 30-minute walk each day, and do a 5-minute relaxation exercise daily. If possible, she should visit the gym one to two times a week. Note this may be a little too much to expect to happen all at once. She might only be able to commit to start with a 5- or 20-minute walk daily. If the plan she lays out is too strict or difficult, she would probably only do it for a few weeks and then *stop* when time doesn't allow. Since her real goal is to achieve regular exercise, let's start with smaller steps.

Jane's Real Goal: To exercise regularly. At first Jane said she wanted to start exercise by going to the gym five days a week. However her lifestyle wouldn't have allowed her to maintain this type of schedule and it would have ultimately have led to no exercise at all. Changing to something that starts small and builds up slowly can allow for a long term healthy habit to take place.

> Start simple with something she can handle and achieve such as taking a 15-minute walk every day.

> If successful for a month, increase the length of her walk a little more. (It takes about a month for a habit to become part of a routine.)

> Each month she should evaluate and redefine her goals and her ability to make it happen.

> She also should always commend herself on anything she does or accomplishes. Any change she makes in the right direction is a good one.

Remember, the real goal here is for her to incorporate more exercise into her life. Throughout the process, she needs to identify the difference between realistic and achievable goals and those that are not currently possible. Reaching her goals one step at a time will prevent her from growing anxious and overwhelming herself which could lead to freeze-ups and failures.

By laying out your plan and accomplishing small goals one at a time, you will land on the finish line of fitness.

FITNESS WORKSHEET:

What fitness goals would you like to create or change today?

_____

_____

_____

_____

_____

How much time can you commit to reaching your goals?

_____

_____

_____

_____

_____

_____

On a scale of 1 to 10 how important is this to you right now or are other things more important now? (If you rank a goal as less than 5, you're likely not ready commit to it.)

_____

_____

_____

_____

_____

_____

Are your goals realistic and reasonable?

_____

_____

_____

_____

_____

_____

What are the actionable steps that you will take to get there?

_____

_____

_____

_____

_____

_____

_____

_____

Chapter IV.
FOOD, FLUID & FIT

In this chapter we will explore the delicate balance between food, fitness and stress management. A whole body approach to health.

The following tools and tips will help you determine the foods, fluids, and activities to include on your journey toward better health. Keep in mind that you are unique. You will need to select the best plan for you and select the changes that you are ready to make now. The choices are yours. If you feel uncertain about where to start, you may find it useful to work with a registered dietitian and personal trainer to find the easiest way to incorporate healthful changes into your life.

Food

Many of us think the word "diet," means weight loss, but the word "diet" really just refers to the types of foods you eat.

When it comes to good nutrition, you may have observed that recommendations for healthy eating has changed many times over the years. That is because as science advances, more information and understanding are unveiled. What to do or not to do is not always black and white because there is so much more to discover. However, there are some basic components that have been recognized that should be considered as a priority in whatever plan you choose.

It's interesting that people differ so much on what they consider to be healthy foods, or what foods they should include in their diet plan. Consider this: if you randomly asked people what they think are healthy dietary choices, their answers will probably not be the same. One person may tell you a high-protein diet, while another is on an all plant-based diet. Another may prefer an organic, non-GMO diet and yet another may fight this and say these changes are not needed. Some people practically live on supplements, not even knowing why they are taking them. They think everything natural is safe, but is it? It may seem confusing, but there are certainties and recommendations that we can be comfortable following because over time they have continued to work and show positive results. What surely doesn't work are *fad* diets which offer quick, big promises, or exclusion diets that eliminate whole food groups (without a diagnosed medical reason). We each need to find our perfect balance.

Healthy Food Choices

Food is the fuel for your body. The following are tried and true healthy dietary recommendations. If you have any health issues, including congestive heart failure or kidney disease, please consult with your doctor and registered dietitian before making any major changes to your diet.

1. If you have a pre-existing health issue, find out if there are any foods that you need to reduce when working on developing your meal plan.

2. Select many different colors when you chose fruits and vegetables and include them daily (each color provides a different health benefit). Increase them as much as possible as long as you can tolerate them and don't have a medical reason to reduce them. Try new selections every day.

3. Use leaner protein choices whenever possible. When selecting fish, purchase more wild-caught fish, not farm-raised fish. (Wild fish aren't pumped up with antibiotics or fed grain and have greater health benefits.)

4. Avoid saturated and trans fats as much as possible.

5. Include more whole grains in your diet. If you are on a gluten-free diet, select gluten-free whole grains and fibers such as amaranth, millet, quinoa, soy, sorghum,

brown rice, buckwheat, beans, and teff.

6. Don't eat your meals late at night. Allow several hours for digestion before going to bed, and try to spread out your food equally throughout the day.

7. Try not to eat over-processed foods and food from fast food restaurants.

8. Watch your sodium (salt and salty food) intake whenever possible.

9. Reduce sweetened foods (such as desserts and candy), as most provide little to no nutritional benefit.

10. Select a wide variety of food groups to include as part of your meal plan. Don't limit your foods to only a few choices or a few categories.

Earlier in this book, I discussed identifying your goals and determining what is realistic. First, take a look at your current diet. Let's face it, we are all creatures of habit and we tend to go back to what we are used to over and over. After all, it is what we are most comfortable with.

Before you go forward with any dietary change,

look at what you are currently doing and then make a list of reasonable healthy alternatives that you are comfortable making.

For example, if you skip meals and then overeat late at night because you're ravenous, you should start eating more throughout the day. This is the easiest way to start. Incorporating small frequent meals spaced several hours apart will keep you from raiding the fridge like you are starving at the end of the day.

Or, do you find that you always pick foods just because you like them and never consider their health benefits? It's best to start your journey by planning a few healthy meals each week. If you are going out to eat a lot, try this trick. Decide what healthier item you will be ordering ahead of time. Don't even listen to the specials or look at the menu when you get to the restaurant. After all, you already have decided what you are going to have. Don't allow yourself to be tempted by looking at other options. Did you ever wonder why sweets and bakery items are in the front of the supermarket or restaurant? To tempt you! And increase sales. If you love bread, you don't have to skip it totally when you go out to eat. Ask the server to bring you one roll instead of the whole bread basket and pass on the butter. If your entrée is a huge portion size, ask for a to-go box as soon as it arrives at the table and before you even start eating. Pack half of your meal up right away. I'm pretty sure you won't go back into that box in the restaurant. If you don't do this first, you may end up eating it all. This surely has happened to you before, *yes*?

Are you so busy that you always just grab food on the run? Start by stocking a lot of healthier, easier to grab items at home and make a list of quick and easy healthy foods that you can pick up when you're out so you have an easy to follow on-the-go list. Make a few healthy meals one day a week so you can just heat-and-serve them whenever needed. A registered dietitian can help you with lots of tips.

Remember any dietary change in a healthy direction can lead to a long-term healthier lifestyle. But for the change to work, it must fit into your current lifestyle to be sustainable as a long-term habit. Generally, if you try to make too many changes at once, you'll have a hard time keeping them up and you may go back to your old habits.

Fluids

Fluids especially water are an essential part of our dietary intake and are required for life. Many people underestimate the importance of drinking more water. Approximately 60 % of your body is made of water. An average person can only survive for about three days without water, but they can go weeks without food. Water is needed for every bodily function to take place. Water helps to regulate body temperature, eliminate waste products, supplies blood volume, lubricates our mucus membranes, support digestive function, improve circulation, ensure skin moisture, and much more. Having adequate fluids helps reduce the likelihood of problems such as: kidney stones (over working the kidneys filter function), urinary tract infections (leaving concentrated bacteria in the bladder), and gout (concentrated levels of uric acid). Having adequate fluids helps our lungs, a mucus membrane, and also makes it easier on our hearts by increasing blood volume.

An average adult needs about 2 to 4 liters of fluid a day. Many variables can increase fluid needs such as age, sex, activity, weight, health issues, outdoor activities, and more. A health care provider can help you to determine how much fluid you need and develop a plan to make sure you stay hydrated. This is especially important when you are on medications or have pre-existing health problems that may require fluid increases or restrictions.

Foods, such as fruits and vegetables, can provide for some of your fluid needs. Water is not the only fluid that will keep you hydrated though it is usually the best choice. Other fluids, including those with electrolytes, will help you to stay hydrated as well.. These are especially good for those who are physically active, do physical work, or participate in sports in the heat. If you have been sweating heavily, you could have lost a lot of potassium and sodium and may require a sports drink or a fluid with specific additions to maintain a healthy hydration level. If you are not doing this heavy physical activity skip on these beverages and skip on the extra calories as well,

Often people will tell me that they drink when they are thirsty. Our antidiuretic hormone let's know when we should drink but for many of us by the time we feel thirsty we are already dehydrated. This is especially true as we age, when our antidiuretic hormone isn't as effective. When I ask my elderly patients if they drink water daily, they say "yes," but when I follow-up for more information I find they only drink when they take their medications, which clearly is not enough to meet their needs.

Signs of inadequate fluid intake include: dark or odorous urine, respiratory issues, dry skin, body aches, headaches, urinary tract infections, kidney stones (not enough fluid to void particles), constipation (from hard stools), gout attacks (from concentrated uric acid), and more.

Drinking adequate fluids daily, especially water is the most important thing we should do for our health. Make a conscious effort to include enough fluids daily.

Stress Management

We all need to balance life's flow. Life has ups and downs. Good stress management means we are able to manage difficulties better when they come up. When you're in balance, your body is in a relaxed, neutral state. When you are not you are in an antagonized stressed state. We all experience stress daily. When that happens our stress response system kicks in, initiating a series of hormonal events in our bodies. This hormonal responses also known as the fight-or-flight response, prepares us to fight off predators or flee from threats. The stress response system is supposed to be triggered only when needed so we can protect ourselves. It should not be perpetually turned "on."

Chronic stress, when your stress response system is turned "on" all the time, puts your health at risk.

Unfortunately for many of us, our day-to-day experiences at work and home are interpreted by our bodies as stress. This triggers our stress response system to initiate fight-or-flight, flooding our body with sugars and hormones, such as adrenaline and cortisol.

Adrenaline increases your heart rate and blood pressure and releases stored energy into your blood supply. This is so we could fight or run when we were in a hostile environment. Increased levels of cortisol raise blood sugars, alter your immune system, slow digestive and reproductive systems, and leads to possible weight gain. Stress can change your mood and motivation levels. When the stress is gone your hormones should return to normal. However, in this world of continuous stress, your hormone levels never equalize, leading to many potential health risks.

Chronic stress contributes to headaches, sleep issues, anxiety, depression, stomach issues, heart disease, lack of clarity of mind, and unusual weight gain or loss. Your genetics can also increase your biological responses to stress even more. In addition when stress is coupled with past negative or traumatic experiences, you may be more likely to expereince fear from harmless triggers, such as a loud noise or crowds, because they serve as a reminder of the past trauma.

What to do? You can't change your body's natural hormonal responses, but you may be able to counteract them by using preventive strategies and stress-reducing activities.

Preventive and Stress Reducing Strategies

The following are strategies to help you reduce and better manage stress:

- Maintain a healthful diet.

- Increase exercise and body movement.

- Get enough sleep.

Avoid stressful triggers.

- Use relaxation techniques such as: Tai chi, mediation, breathing exercises, yoga, massage, peaceful music, enjoyable hobbies.

- Have more fun.

- Continue spiritual pursuits.

- See friends more often.

- Laugh more.

- Seek counseling if needed.

- Take any medications as prescribed.

Stress can kill, so it is essential that you incorporate these strategies daily to lower its potential damage to your body.

I have experienced a physical reaction due to stress several times in my life. The response was so evident, it was impossible to ignore. The first time it occurred when I was very young. Our family experienced the tragic loss of my brother, only 18 months younger than me. After his death, I was unable to function in social situations. I became ill quite often and then experienced the symptoms which are commonly referred to as failure to thrive. It took me years to overcome the fall-out and move forward. Later in life when my mother passed I thought I was actually handling things okay. However, the exact same month that she died, I went into instant and complete menopause. No symptoms, just post-menopausal in only one month.

Our bodies are machines. Even when we think we are able to handle the stressors around us we may not be able to do so. We are genetically programmed to handle our environment in a specific physical way. It is only when we incorporate preventative strategies that we will be able to handle the stress around us better helping to prevent it from becoming chronic. By incorporating stress reducing activities into our lives daily we reduce the harsh health outcomes of prolonged stress.

Physical Fitness

The importance of physical fitness cannot be underestimated. We are designed to move our bodies. However, for many of us our day-to-day functions provide our bodies with little to no movement at all. Even a small amount of daily exercise has benefits which contribute to optimal health.

Exercise helps you to:

- maintain a normal body weight.

- maintain lower blood pressure.

- achieve normal cholesterol levels.

- lower blood sugars.

- improve cardiac function.

- reduce body pain from muscle aches.

- strengthen your bones.

- increase respiratory function.

- reduce stress.

- feel happier and less depressed.

- sleep better.

- relax more.

- increase your energy.

- increase your cognitive function.

- reduce your risk of chronic disease.

Most of us can agree that we would all like to experience the benefits listed above. Our bodies need to do what they are designed to do in order to function optimally. We all need to find a way to move more. Even if you are bedridden, you can do stretches to keep your body moving. If you are in pain and that is why you don't exercise consider this, lack of movement usually leads to more pain.

If you have a pre-existing health problem or are on medications, you should talk to your health care provider about which exercises are safe for you to do before diving into a new activity. When you start your exercise plan, take it slow; don't push yourself and risk an injury. Increase exercise at your own pace. If you are someone who has a pre-existing injury that prevents you from participating in some types of exercise, find an alternative instead. For example, if you have a problem with your feet or with your knees, you may need to do your exercises while seated or exercises like biking or swimming which are easier on the feet and knees.

Here are a few additional tips for bringing more movement into your life:

- Go slow and steady. If you push yourself too much or too hard, you could injure yourself.

- Find an activity that you like and that fits into your daily routine. You'll be much more likely to stick with it. If you plan to exercise during your lunch break, you should make sure your gym is near your office or there is a nearby place where you can take a walk. If you hate the gym, consider hiking, dancing, or even kayaking as an alternative. In other words, to succeed in the long run, you need to find something that works for you.

- Mix it up. It is important to do a combination of different types of exercise to support different parts of your body.

The most important thing to remember are, to move your body more every day, find something that you like and stick with it. You will start feeling better and stronger right away.

FOOD & FITNESS WORKSHEET:

It is important to do a health self-evaluation to set you on the right path.

FOOD

How many of the top ten healthy food tips do you follow daily? Where do you think you can improve?

_____

_____

_____

_____

_____

FLUIDS

How much fluid do you consume on a daily basis?

_____

_____

_____

_____

_____

STRESS

How many of the stress reducing strategies mentioned in this chapter do you do every week and how often?

_____

_____

_____

_____

_____

_____

_____

Can you list all the things that stress you on an average day?

_____

_____

_____

_____

Do you feel you have any physical symptoms of stress?

_____

_____

_____

_____

Can you think of ways to reduce some of your daily stressors?

_____

_____

_____

_____

Physical Fitness

Exercise is essential for good health. What are the most important fitness goals you would like to reach?

_____

_____

_____

_____

_____

_____

_____

What types of exercise would you be able to incorporate into your daily routine?

_____

_____

_____

_____

_____

_____

_____

Chapter V. FAMILY, FRIENDS & FUN

Family and friends provide a strong, solid foundation on which we can build a stable, focused life. They can raise our self-esteem and give us the strength to face the trials and tribulations of life. Without this supportive foundation, it is much more difficult to reach our full potential. Good relationships with your family and friends can provide joy-filled memories that will last a lifetime and comfort you when you feel lost or hopeless.

Some of us have strong relationships in one or both of these categories. Family is family for life, and you may be close to your entire family or just to a few members. You may have family members who drive you crazy, yet you still love them. The old line, "you can't pick your family," has truth at its core.

On the other side, you may have family members who you are close to, but they live so far away that it limits your time with them. You may want to develop relationships with those who live closer to you to give you daily support through connections and communications.

Remember nothing is set. Family memories can be good or bad. Family members can be supportive and loving or they can be hurtful and disruptive. Each person has different memories to draw from. In any case, in order to reach your full potential in life, you will thrive better in a supportive, loving environment with people who make you feel safe. If you have good family relationships, you can become even stronger and happier by also building close friendships. If you do not have family relationships that support you in the way that you need them to, then turn to close friends and make them your extended family. One of the definitions of friendship is someone you hold in high regard, whom you trust and who cares about your psychological welfare.

I cannot overstate the importance of having an "A" team that you can count on. It's never too late to build relationships. When you build your friendships, you want to establish relationships with people whom you trust and with whom you share mutual respect. If you trust them, you can feel okay sharing your vulnerable moments with them. Good friends care about your beliefs even when they differ from theirs. They are there for you when you are stressed or when you are down and at your weakest. They are able to help you to rebound from your difficulties and can change your mood easily. True friendship develops into ties that can last a lifetime. And true friends will be there for you even if you have nothing left to offer them.

Remember when I did my time assessment in Chapter II? I didn't have enough time for the people I cared about most. I had to trim down my daily chores in order to find time for them.

What is the point of this life journey if all my time is used up on work, chores, and to dos? Make each day count by spending time with the people you love and care about. This is what truly brings *joy*. We should always seek to hit our maximum joy potential.

To achieve true happiness, spend more of your time with those you are close to. Relationships are part of your footprints in the sand. You can draw your strength from them when needed. They can support your dreams, provide direction, carry you when you are down, nurture you, and provide joyful moments. They can help you build your most cherished memories. They can help you in times of stress, sorrow, and difficulties. They can share their love and bring you back from the dark side. Those who are true friends and loving family members will fight for you, cry with you, pray with you, and stick with you through thick and thin.

It is true that you can survive without these people in your life but who would want to? You may feel safer by not allowing yourself to be vulnerable to others, but by allowing others to be part of your foundation you will become a stronger person. If tragedy causes a crack in your base, they can help you to patch it up and rebuild. When you are down and everything is falling apart, close relationships are the glue that keeps things together. They are there for you, helping to improve your mood and build-up your confidence even before you realize you need the support.

Of course, relationships are not all about you. It is give and take; you need to give as much as you get. In true friendships, you will always treat your friends as you would like to be treated yourself. True friendships are built on trust, mutual respect, and unconditional love and will pay out dividends more then you could ever wish for, dream of, or imagine.

Building Healthy Relationships

A relationship is like a plant. The plant may grow even if you neglect it but, it will never reach its full potential without care, sunlight, food, and water. Our relationships also need continued care to grow.

Traits of a Healthy Relationship:

- Trust (believe in each other, true honesty)

- Love (unconditional, caring, feelings)

- Committed (there through it all)

- Acceptance (you take the good and the bad)

- Laughter (it brings you true joy)

- Consistent (you can count on each other, through thick and thin)

- Vulnerability (safety and additional trust)

- Be There (support when needed)

- Openness (to new ideas and thoughts)

- Listen (hear all you say, not just their pre-summary)

- Loyal (you are always on each other's side)

- Flexibility (will try to change for each other when needed)

- Saying sorry and being accountable (admits mistakes and forgives)

- Complement (reinforce positive things)

- Mutual Respect (regard for each other's feelings)

- Give and Take (give unconditionally to each other)

- Compromise (find a middle ground)

- Communication (free information exchange)

- Connection (allowing true feelings to grow)

No relationship is perfect but healthy ones will continue to work through problems and will develop and grow over time.

If you have been cautious in the past about opening yourself up to close relationships, you may want to reconsider. I encourage you to do so. Try with small steps. Begin by opening yourself to trust just a little at a time. True friendships will show their benefits as you let them in. It's okay if you've let toxic people into your inner circle in the past. We all have! Start fresh now. If you still have toxic people in your life, let them go and move on.

It's never too late to start building healthy, close relationships if you don't feel you have them. Find new friends by, joining support groups with that have members who have similar interests as you. Or why not pick up new hobbies, and become active in associations and groups. Be open to getting to know new people. Go slow, one step at a time, and always make sure you feel safe.

Unhealthy Relationships

Unhealthy relationships are toxic. Run. If your relationships share any of the following traits, they are not healthy and they can hurt more than help. Toxic relationships usually cannot be easily fixed.

Instead, limit your interactions with people who behave poorly to you. People usually don't change—even if they say they will.

Traits of Unhealthy Relationships:

- Ridicule (or make fun of)

- Criticize (always looking to say something negative)

- Put Down (especially in front of others)

- Threatening (to reveal or embarrass publicly)

- Always Right (thereby saying you are always wrong)

- Should on You (always telling you what you should do and never allowing you to be yourself)

- Poor Communicator and Poor Listener (discounting the importance of what you have to say)

- Not Open or Loving (no closeness)

- Close Minded (I am right and I don't need to listen to you)

- Cold (uninterested and lack responsiveness)

- Selfish (all about them)

- Temper (shows displays of anger freely)

- Betrayal (can't be trusted, turns secrets against you)

- Lies (can't believe what they say)

It's possible that someone can have mostly good attributes and one of the negative items noted above. But if the traits on this list remind you of your relationship with someone who you think is a friend, you need to consider limiting your time with them or moving on.

Any friendship will have its ups and downs. The give and take of forgiveness, connection, and compromise will carry you forward into the future together. When these traits aren't there, it's time to leave that relationship in the past.

Fun

Don't underestimate the importance of fun and play in your life. I mentioned the benefits of fun earlier in the book as part of your fitness profile. Fun provides many of the joys of life. Research has found that fun and play can be the baseline of happiness. Most adults get so tied up with their chores every day that they often overlook this. Kids seem to do fun things daily, but adults sometimes act as if they forgot how to play. Below are some ways to incorporate more fun into your life. Remember when you were younger and you really didn't need big plans to enjoy a day? It could be just meeting and walking around with your friends or listening to music and letting the day play out. Think back to those days now and the simple pleasures you enjoyed.

Ideas for Having Fun

- Do something silly.

- Don't be afraid to laugh out loud.

- Don't be afraid to laugh at yourself.

- Hang out with fun people.

- Incorporate some fun into your work.

- Tell a joke or go to a comedy event.

- Do something new or different that you've never done before.

- Do something you haven't done since childhood.

- Play a game.

- Create an art project.

- Be spontaneous.

- Try a new (safe) sport.

- Be less inhibited.

- Have a day with nothing planned except the quest for play and fun.

People who have more fun and laugh more: live longer, get sick less often, are less angry, let go of things easier, have fewer conflicts, better memory, happier family lives and relationships, less stress, and fewer hormonal imbalances. In addition, they enjoy their time more and have more friends.

Everyone enjoys different things, and you may not like everything you try, but no matter what, try to do something fun that you enjoy every day.

FAMILY, FRIENDS, FUN WORKSHEET:

What do you value the most out of your relationships with family and friends?

_____

_____

_____

_____

Are your relationships healthy or unhealthy and what changes do you need to make in the future?

_____

_____

_____

_____

_____

Do you include fun as part of your daily activities?

_____

_____

_____

_____

_____

What positive steps can you make to include more fun into your life daily?

_____

_____

_____

_____

_____

_____

_____

Chapter VI. FEAR

When you think of the word "Fearful" do you think of it as a bad thing? How about when you hear the word "FEARLESS." Does it seem good? It's not so simple though. Being fearful can be a positive just as being fearless can be a negative. Even though they seem far apart there is a fine line between fearful and fearless. It isn't always so simple to say which one you would want to be? The meaning of the word FEAR can change depending on how far to the right or left side of the spectrum you are.

You may be asking yourself, why is there a chapter about fear in a book about life balance? Fear is more intertwined into moving forward then you think. It is at those moments when life seems to be falling apart and everything is going wrong that fears can grow and fester. When everything is stressing us out we might throw in the towel and give up, or we may become totally desperate and do something crazy. We can slide either way on the drop of a dime.

Think about it. Success gives you wings to explore and be more adventurous and failure stops you cold from ever trying again. If you had been a profitable investor until one day when you lost most of your money by investing in a company that turned out to be a scam, you might be so afraid of ever investing again that you take your money out of the bank and hide it under your mattress. Or would you look to a professional for help? Would you seek out a very cautious accountant to help you, or a smooth-talking salesman?

Your past experiences often change the way you look at things, making you look for either a safe or exciting next move. We could say that loss of confidence can lead to fear. If we fall off a horse and don't get right back on, the fear of falling again could build and grow, creating triggers that keep us off a horse for life. Someone who is extremely fearful may be frightened, anxious, worrisome, and/or depressed at times.

Or maybe the opposite happens. Someone who was always a little fearless became more so because their fearlessness led to positive experiences. These positive experiences reinforced the benefits of being fearless. They may be brave, courageous, adventurous, and bold.

Remember the old saying, "You have nothing to fear but fear itself?" It holds true in some cases, but in others you really do need to be a little extra careful and just a little fearful to be safe. You can be both a little fearful and a little fearless at the same time.

If you saw the movie *Raiders of The Lost Ark,* you may remember that Indiana Jones was daring and unafraid of everything, the bravest of the brave, willing to venture everywhere—until he saw there were snakes around. He then said the classic line, "Why did they have to be snakes?" Clearly something happened in his past to make this courageous man's man afraid of snakes. He was fearless and fearful at the same time.

By understanding how fear operates, you can use it to your benefit.

What does this mean for you? Let's take this thought one step further and put things into an actionable perspective. Let's look at things on scale where 5 is the middle or neutral and you can go up to 10 as being maxed out (see diagram). Therefore if you were so fearful or frightened of something that on a scale of 5 to 10 and you were a 10, you might become paralyzed. Even the thought of it could hit a trigger that brings you to a non-functional state. There are situations where your fear could become so intense that you might even be afraid to leave your house, or maybe you're so terrified of spiders that you won't go into your basement, or you might drive thousands of miles because you are afraid to fly. Sometimes that intense fear can hit so hard it makes it impossible for someone to function. For example, someone is so afraid of becoming ill they never go to the doctor because there could be bad news. Because they never go to the doctor, they don't find out about an illness that was treatable until it is in the advanced stages. The fear can actually freeze them so much that it might actually bring them to a negative outcome or a self-fulfilling prophecy.

Of course if you were just a little fearful of something, you would still be able to function and you might just be a little more careful and do more research before jumping into something. So you would go to the doctor, but you would also research to go to the best.

What about being fearless? If you were so fearless that on a scale of 5 to 10 and you were a 10, you could be so reckless you might try to jump Niagara Falls with a motorcycle (Evel Knievel) or climb the Empire State Building or risk your entire life savings in the stock market on risky investments or at the tables in Las Vegas.

By contrast, if you take that #10 of fearlessness and pivot it over to a 7, you might be fearless enough to be brave and to go into things with confidence but just a bit more careful than a 10. When you go forward with a little caution, it can help to make the outcome more stable. Being sure of yourself or slightly fearless can help you to move forward but too much fearlessness could be dangerous.

Too far on either end of the fear scale is not a good

way to live, a little pivot toward the middle is the smarter move.

No matter where you are on the scale from 5 to 10, you could create change in your life by pivoting one or two notches closer to 5, a balanced medium. When your fearfulness goes from a 10 to an 8 or your fearlessness goes from a 10 to an 8, you will see and embrace life from an whole new level. Think about the types of changes you could expect and how they would adjust how you adapt to roadblocks in your path.

Navigating fear is like finding the balance between good and bad or hot and cold. A small step toward the middle could be a great new place to be.

So, let's redefine fearfulness and fearlessness:

Fearfulness: A little fear could make someone more careful; they would research more, plan things out more, and be slow and steady. But if something makes them really afraid and totally fearful, they may never do anything new, never invest, and may not put themselves in a position to change ever again. Fearfulness could be a good or bad thing.

Fearlessness: Someone who is just a little fearless could be a hero or a calculated high-risk investor, and they may be willing to try many new things.

However, if they felt totally fearless and able to try or do *anything*, they may end up in a very dangerous situation. They might be so heroic that they do not survive their heroism. They might be so reckless that they lose their house in a card game. Too much fearlessness could be a good or bad thing.

Instead of thinking in absolutes, consider the power of a small pivot to bring you closer to balance.

The Benefits of Balance

Since fearfulness and fearlessness can be good or bad we should all strive to pivot just one notch closer to a 5. This one small change can get us to look at life just a little bit differently, opening us up to new situations and opportunities. If you were heartbroken and swore never to love again, maybe one notch over will let you try it again; isn't it worth it? It's okay to be a little afraid (careful, planned out, long term, slow, and steady) and it could be a good thing to be a little fearless, (outgoing, adventurous, brave, and daring).

Many of us stay in one mindset for most of our lives, which keeps us from being able to see beyond our own limiting thoughts.

Where do you fit on this scale?

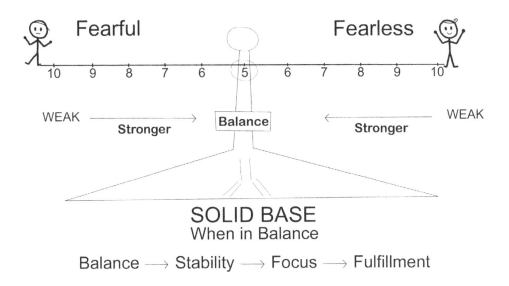

SOLID BASE
When in Balance

Balance ⟶ Stability ⟶ Focus ⟶ Fulfillment

When you look at this model, it is clear that either person can pivot a little toward the center toward a healthier balance. A little tilt can provide excitement, joy, and new possibilities.

But you might not want to be balanced and completely neutral. Let's say you are a professional speaker who is just slightly afraid in front of an audience. That fear might be interpreted as energy by the audience. Keeping your fearfulness or fearlessness at a 6 or 7 might serve you well.

Let's say you work in sales. Being a 5 may not give you the edge you need to generate new business.

As a 7 on the fearless side, you are confident and able to maintain your edge while not being as pushy or overbearing as you would be as a 10. For you, being a 7 strikes the right balance.

We all should try to pivot our lives one notch closer to neutral to give us just a little more balance but you need to find the right balance for you.

Balance allows you to get the most out of life. If you allow yourself to change just a little, you will experience more benefits than you ever imagined.

In the beginning of this book, I spoke about Newton's law of motion. An object at rest remains at rest or in a straight line unless something changes its path. Consider yourself to be moving along in a straight line unless you allow something new in.

Earlier on I shared some of my personal history and the paralyzing hits to my life—one after another. Everything went wrong. It was like dodging bullets from a machine gun. Frightening.

I was so paralyzed from life events that I couldn't find the rope that I needed to pull myself out of the hole I was in. I was stuck. That jarring experience on the staircase and with my client helped me to see things clearly and I was able to pivot 2 notches over to the fearless side and start fresh in a new, empowered place.

Whenever you feel stuck, try to visualize where you are on the Fearful/Fearless Scale, and then move yourself over a notch, like a piece on a chess board, allowing yourself to evolve and change.

FEAR WORKSHEET:

On the scale of 1 to 10, where do you stand between Fearful and Fearless?

_____

_____

_____

In what area of your life would you like to be more Fearful? Fearless?

_____

_____

_____

_____

What does balance look like for you on the Fearful/Fearlessness Scale? What can you do to achieve it?

_____

_____

_____

_____

_____

_____

_____

Chapter VII. FINANCE

What do you consider financial stability? Are you financially stable if you have enough money to live on, the ability to pay your bills, or the ability to buy anything you ever wanted? How much money is really enough?

Being financially successful is all about balance and direction. Balance is what you are comfortable with and direction is where you want to end up.

I can say with 100% certainty that my definition of financial success has changed throughout my life. If you would have asked me when I was a little girl how much money I wanted when I grew up, I would have said I wanted to be rich. If you asked me what would be enough money in my 20s, I would tell you I wanted to own an island. In my 30s, I wanted a house on an island. In my 40s, I wanted to be able to retire comfortably in 10 to 15 years. In my 50s, I wanted to be able to pay my bills without stress, have enough money to retire, and some surplus to take a few nice trips every year.

Life is constantly changing and so are you. The two most important questions that you can ask yourself about your finances are: what do I need financially to make me happy today and what do I want in the future? If you can answer these questions honestly, it is easier to figure out how to get what you want. Next, follow the steps outlined in Chapters I and II to find your focus, establish your priorities, and create an action plan. When you break down your action plan into small workable steps, you can plan for both short- and long-term financial goals and timelines.

Step 1. Set your priorities so you know where you want to go.

Step 2. Put your priorities in order of importance.

Step 3. Identify exactly what each priority means to you.

Step 4. Break down each priority into small actionable steps.

Step 5. Determine if you have the time and resources to implement your plan.

Step 6. Find the time you need.

Step 7. Decide how to spend your time.

Step 8. Change as needed.

If you are caught in a windstorm of life events, you may find it difficult to get a handle on your financial matters and change course. Right now, you just need to keep your feet on the ground. Any positive step is a good move. It's important to address any problems that are making it impossible to move ahead, such as: If you found yourself buried in credit card debt. In this situation you could be paying out so many payments and so much interest every month that you can't get ahead of your debt. The easiest way to start is to consolidate your expenses with one creditor. By doing this you would lower the interest and monthly payments into something which may be more manageable to pay off. This way you can get grounded and be clear minded when you set a new strategy for going forward. The most important thing is to stabilize first before you make any major changes. If you don't address the problems, you'll find it almost impossible to achieve a positive cash flow and a safe, stable direction. First, find out what you need to stay afloat and then take baby steps going forward.

Get help if you need it. You may not have the background to create and implement a financial action plan on your own. Use an expert such as the ones mentioned below. Don't try to do everything yourself.

Accountant

A good accountant does more than your tax returns. Accountants are financial professionals who can provide ideas, isolate your spending, give realistic feedback, work on retirement funds, and help you plan for your future. They can explain the tax advantages of different moves, organize your financial tracking systems, and even help you finance your ideas.

Certified Financial Planner

It pays to have a consultant who will work with you to present many different options and opportunities—even if you are a savvy investor. There are different types of degrees and certifications for financial planning; be sure to investigate these before hiring. A certified financial planner is a highly-regarded credential. Asking for referrals is the best first step when selecting someone. A certified financial planner could give you new ideas to diversify your portfolio. They can also evaluate changes in the marketplace and give you feedback on your investment ideas. You don't have to do everything they recommend, but it does help to get feedback from a professional before making any big moves.

Information Technology (IT) Support

A tech expert can help you in so many ways. They can keep your network and computers working properly and identify apps, promotional resources, programs, and search engines that will make it possible for you to do your work more efficiently. When doing your day-to-day and tracking your money is easier, you will have the opportunity to spend your time and money more effectively, leading you to a better career or business. If you don't have access to IT or hiring an IT specialist is price prohibitive, you can get help from students who are studying in this field at a much lower rate.

Lawyers

There are legal ramifications for most business plans. If you are trying to build a financial future you need to protect your assets. There are times you may need copyrights, trademarks, and contract reviews. If you work for a company there may be restrictive clauses, job requirements, and limits that are in the contracts that they ask you to sign when you are hired. Knowing how to read these documents can have a significant impact on your financial future. If you can't afford a lawyer, join one of the many legal groups that will give you contracts, reviews, and consulting at very reasonable rates. Many lawyers will give you a free consult on the phone or in person before the clock starts ticking; you can learn a lot on these free consults. Legal representation is an important way to protect your work and is essential for future financial success.

Additional Resources

There are companies to help you plan ahead in so many areas, ranging from your retirement, to your will, to consolidations, to depreciations, and to moving and growing your investments. Having a team that you can run things by will help you to make better decisions. Having more professionals helping you gives you access to many of their contacts.

What if you have no money to hire professional help? Don't despair. There are many non-profit business support organizations that offer free or low-cost training provided by retired business executives. Often these professionals are more than happy to share their ideas and experience with you. Groups include: The Better Business Bureau, Vistage Executive Coaching, Scope Business Coaching, and more are available to offer their help.

Here are a few additional tips for when you are focused on your financial needs:

> - Don't take advice from just anyone. There is always someone who will tell you what you should or shouldn't do. Instead, get some professional help. It's always better to get feedback from two or more professionals before you make any big moves.

> - Be careful about making large sudden changes. Instead, try to keep your changes to small steps. Give it time and don't expect things to happen overnight.

> - Reset and refocus whenever needed. Collect information as you build you assets and change things around if you see that your plan isn't working for you.

Getting it Together Financially

To make money you need to spend money. But you can't spend money you don't have.

Remember in Chapter II when we did the time assessment to figure out how much time you spend on your daily activities and where you could trim back on wasted time so you could accomplish your goals? Before making any financial changes, you should know where your finances stand now and do a similar assessment to determine how much money you have, how you spend it, and where you could cut back in order to have enough money to achieve your financial priorities. Use these steps to do a financial assessment:

1. Create a detailed list of what you earn. Make sure you include all sources of income, including freelance work.

2. Track your spending for at least two weeks, including all of those extra expenses you may not usually pay attention to, such as takeout meals, snacks, and beverages.

3. Determine if there are expenses you could reduce or eliminate to save money. This may mean canceling or changing a service, purchasing less expensive items or only items on sale, cutting up your credit cards, not ordering supplies until you really need

them, or downsizing your car or your home. Most people wait too long to change their spending habits and find themselves deeply in debt.

4. You may find that even with cutbacks, you may not be netting as much as you thought (or want). Consider how else you could bring in more money. A part-time job? Changes to the way you do business?

If you are financially stable and your financial goals are to build on that foundation, you could skip this assessment but I suggest doing it anyway. It's good to know as much as possible about your finances when things are going well so you are prepared if life throw you a curveball.

How to reboot or increase financial stability

This plan has rebooted and increased my own and my clients' financial stability time and time again. When my business and life took a big hit, I used this plan to get both back on track—and more than doubled my business in one year. There are three principles:

- **Work With What You Have**

- **Plan For What You Want**

- **So You Can Live What You Dream**

Work with what you have: There are always things you may want to change: your job, your house, your clothes, your savings. There are so many things you may want. Those wants won't help you to achieve your goals, though. Instead, you need to work with what you have *now*. Knowing what you already have (skills, assets, customers, contacts, etc.) makes it possible to build up some stability. For example, if you are unhappy at your current job, look for a new job while you are still employed. If you have an existing business, ask yourself: What is good about it? Is it worth it for me to put time, energy, and money into it, or do I need to close it and make a living elsewhere? Once you've assessed what you have, you can determine if what you have right now can help you achieve your financial goals. If it won't, you may need to change what you're doing now in order to cover your daily needs and give yourself room to build. This type of planning goes far beyond money. When you work with what you have, you must consider where you live, your outside relationships, your skills, etc. You need to work with *everything* you have in order to grow.

Plan for what you want: When you made your priority list and defined your actionable steps earlier in this book, you determined what you want and made a list of steps and time changes needed to get there. It is prudent to be stable while you are working to reach your goals and desires. Once you set some stability by working with what you have, you can work on planning for what you want. Take small steps, stay on your path, adjust to handle your obstacles, and you will be walking toward what you want.

So you can live what you dream: If you truly know what you want and you keep heading toward it, while making small turns along the way, you have given yourself the strongest possible start to get part or all of what you dream of in your future. Things can change, even your dreams, so review your choices as you go in case your wants have also changed.

When you use this action plan, you have given yourself the best chance for the future that you have wished for.

The Illusion

Often, those who should be in a good financial situations don't seem stable. Do you know people who make more than enough money to cover all their needs and yet they are always broke? Through the years I have worked with many individuals who were earning huge amounts of money, but they never seemed to have enough to pay all of their bills and had little to nothing saved. When we investigated their finances more closely, we discovered the problem—a huge underestimation of their daily spending.

On paper they earned more than enough to cover their monthly bills and then some. But the extras that they thought were just bits of money here and there added up to far more than they could have ever imagined. It's the "little" expenses we don't pay much attention to that add up, such as going out to eat, online shopping, gifts and treating friends, weekends away, outdoor activities, and buying the newest electronic devices. So many people never kept track of these costs. Did you ever have a lot of money in your checking account and it just seemed to disappear even though you thought you hadn't bought anything and had nothing to show for it? These folks did. They just couldn't see how they were throwing away all their surplus funds. Eyes they have, but see not. These so-called "small extras" were eating up everything they earned plus some, and they were going into debt. Don't overlook these types of expenses as you assess your finances.

Money problems trickle down and affect so many other parts of our lives. When we suffer financially it may hurt other things, too. Maybe we can't fix an appliance in our house, buy new clothes for our children, take a vacation, or afford health insurance. Couples most often fight about money. Having stable finances benefits you and everyone in your life and can sometimes improve your quality of life.

Helping Steve

Remember Steve from Chapter I? Steve wanted to work a regular day job and spend time with his wife and 4-year-old daughter but he was stuck working at his father's struggling business. He previously had many employment opportunities and could easily earn a good salary at a regular 9 to 5-type job with benefits. But Steve couldn't say "no" to his father when he asked for his help so now Steve works all the time, makes little money, and is rarely home to spend time with his wife and daughter.

Let's help Steve pivot to a new place. First Steve worked on focus by evaluating his priorities, putting them into priority order and identifying his actionable steps to go forward. What he found was so simple. He needed to find a way to leave his father's business without hurting it and he needed a new job in the field he was trained for.

Work With What You Have: Steve knows his father's business and also has experience and connections in the field that he would like to go back to. First he is looking to find someone to replace him at his dads shop. He needs to find someone who is capable and with the level of experience commiserate with the salary his dad's business can afford. Steve will train them to make sure they understand the support his father needs. Steve also has maintained a strong network of business contacts and he plans to now tap into them to secure a job in a company that can offer a good salary with a pension, vacation time, and health insurance.

Plan For What You Want: Now that Steve has a better job, he has more time for his family. Which is all he ever wanted. He feels good about his move especially since he helped stabilize his dads company with a quality employee which he helped to train. So now Steve can plan to move up in his field while taking care of his family's needs.

So You Can Live What You Dream: By helping his dad find good employee and working with them, Steve is supporting his dad. By making the job change, Steve is now in a better financial state and has time for his family. Steve is living his dream of a happier, fuller life which meets his goals and priorities.

Make decisions and changes that support your long-term goals as much as possible. Don't let yourself get stuck in an unhappy place. With proper planning, you can help create your own financially stable future.

FINANCE WORKSHEET:

Make a list of your current financial earnings and your current expenses.

_____

_____

_____

_____

_____

_____

If you are spending more than you earn, where can you reduce expenses?

_____

_____

_____

_____

_____

What do you have? List all your financial assets, connections, talents, skills, etc.

_____

_____

_____

What do you want for your future (financial and personal wants)? List the steps you can take to get there:

_____

_____

_____

_____

_____

Do you need outside resources or help to take these steps?

_____

_____

_____

What are your dreams? What are you striving for?

_____

_____

_____

_____

_____

_____

_____

Chapter VIII. FINDING YOUR Future

You have taken the first steps on your quest to reach a healthy life balance.

As you move forward, remember the key areas to focus on:

- Fitness

- Family/Friends

- Fun

- Finance

Define your goals, do self-assessments, set actionable steps, and make changes as life changes. We are all different and we each need to find the path that works best for us. Build bridges to overcome obstacles, identify your strengths, and review and change your goals and objectives to help tailor your goals to what works best for you. Any movement can take you to a new place, so embrace that which comes your way. That small step may help you see things from a different angle. Bridge the gap between fearfulness and fearlessness, ask for help when you need it, and strive to reach your dreams. Above all always remember:

Work with What You Have

Plan for What You Want

So You Can Live What You Dream

ABOUT THE AUTHOR

Marlisa Brown is a registered dietitian, certified diabetes educator, professional speaker, author, and chef. She has served as president of Total Wellness Inc. for more than 2 ½ decades. She has a BS in marketing and an MS in nutrition. Marlisa has helped over 20,000 clients successfully achieve a healthy life balance. Her nutritional practice specializes in diabetes, obesity, cardiac disorders, gastrointestinal issues, and motivational work.

Some of her clients include: individuals and universities such as Binghamton, Adelphi, and CW Post; professional sports teams such as the NY Jets; corporations such as Prudential Securities, Goldman Sachs, Chase, and Guardian Life; celebrities such as Richard Simmons, Kathy Smith, and Jorge Cruise; and food service companies such as Lackmann Culinary Services where she was the Wellness Coordinator for ten years.

Marlisa has given hundreds of presentations, made numerous television appearances, coordinated healthful marketing events, and created multi-million dollar health programs, educational promotions, and corporate wellness programs for clients. She has contributed to many publications, written five books including *Gluten-Free Hassle-Free* and *Easy Gluten-Free*. She has worked with major media publications, and has ghostwritten additional books and programs for numerous celebrities.

Marlisa is a member of many professional organizations including the Academy of Nutrition and Dietetics, the American Diabetes Association, the American Association of Diabetes Educators, the International Association of Culinary Professionals, the National Speakers Association, Meeting Planners International, and the Gluten Intolerance Group, among others.

Marlisa has served on many BODs including as past president, media representative, and public relations chair for the New York State Academy of Nutrition and Dietetics. She received the 2011 Diabetes Educator of the Year Award from the Diabetes Care and Education group, the Emerging Dietetic Leader Award from the Academy of Nutrition and Dietetics, Dietitian of the Year from the Long Island Dietetic Association, Best Of Long Island from the *Long Island Press*, and the Community Service Award from C.W. Post.

To find out what Marlisa can do for you or your organization, contact her at:

Total Wellness Inc.

375 Commack Rd

Suite #201

Deer Park, NY 11729

631-666-4297

Email: MarlisaSpeaks@gmail.com

Twitter: @MarlisaRD

Linked In: https://www.linkedin.com/in/marlisa-brown/

Instagram: @marlisabrown8

www.MarlisaSpeaks.com

www.TWellness.net

www.GlutenFreeEZ.com

36250152R00080

Made in the USA
Middletown, DE
15 February 2019